THE SECOND Garfield SUPER TREASURY

JIM DAVIS

WH SMITH

EXCLUSIVE · BOOKS ·

Produced exclusively for WHSmith Limited by
Ravette Books Limited 1990.

Printed and bound for Ravette Books Limited,
3 Glenside Estate, Star Road,
Partridge Green, Nr. Horsham,
West Sussex RH13 8RA
by Mateu Cromo Artes Gráfica, s.a.

ISBN: 1 85304 281 1

10-7   JIM DAVIS

HEY, HUBERT! REBA! COME HERE, QUICK!

PLAY COWBOY AND HORSY, BOYS. DO A HANDSTAND, GARFIELD. BALANCE ON GARFIELD, ODIE

SAD

HE SHOULD GET OUT OF THE HOUSE MORE

© 1987 United Feature Syndicate, Inc.

JiM DAViS 8-30

© 1987 United Feature Syndicate, Inc.   JIM DAVIS 9-20

RUN FOR YOUR LIFE! IT'S A RABID MUSKRAT!

I LIKE THE PART WHERE HE MADE YOU FETCH IT ON ALL FOURS

OH, SHUT UP

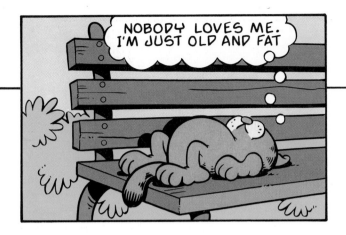

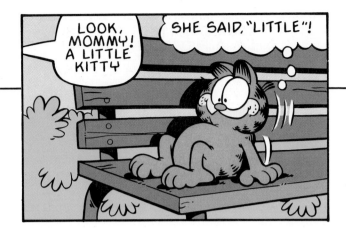

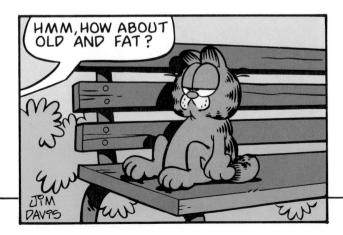

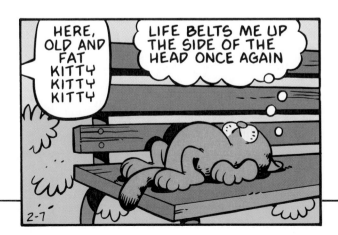